New
READING
360
PLAYS

Thingumybob

Steve Barlow and Steve Skidmore

Illustrated by
Mark Burgess

Series Editors
Steve Barlow and Steve Skidmore

Thingumybob

When Mr Mann starts to take the class register, it looks like the start of any ordinary school day. Several pupils are missing, though. One by one they turn up with the news that something dreadful is loose in the town! Is it a Thingumybob, a Watchamacallit, an Oojamaflip – or is it just an excuse for being late? Mr Mann doesn't believe his pupils, but teachers aren't always right...

The Characters

Mr Mann

He isn't a nasty teacher, it's just that he never has time for everything he's got to do, so he gets cross when he thinks people in his class are telling tall stories. He really doesn't deserve the horrible fate that happens to him!

Miss Pelling

She doesn't get upset about things as easily as Mr Mann, and is much more careful to listen to what the children say, which is just as well for her!

Creepy Claire

Claire is the school sneak. She is always trying to get people into trouble. If anyone deserves to meet the Thingumybob, it's Claire.

Jason

Jason is a very nervous boy – he is scared to death of the Thingumybob, but he still wants to hear all about it.

Andy, Denise, Gabriel, Louise and Surinder

They are all pupils in Mr Mann's class who have seen the Thingumybob and can't wait to tell the others all the details. They are all quite ordinary – in fact, they are almost exactly like the people who are playing them.

Mr Mann

Miss Pelling

Creepy Claire

Jason

Andy

Denise

Gabriel

Louise

Surinder

Alan, Amy, Bernard, Emma, Katy, Michaela and Peter
More pupils in Mr Mann's class. They answer the register when their names are called, but the really important thing they have to do is to show how frightened they are when the others are telling Mr Mann about the Thingumybob.

Mr Mann: Come along, come along, class. Sit down please and BE QUIET!

(The pupils quieten down.)

Mr Mann: That's better. Now, let's see who's here. Alan?

Alan: Here, sir.

Mr Mann: Amy?

Amy: Here, sir.

Mr Mann: Andy?

(There is no reply.)

Mr Mann: Andy? Where's Andy?

Whole Class: Don't know, sir.

Creepy Claire: Will he get his name in the Bad Book, sir?

(Andy rushes in late, very hot and bothered.)

Mr Mann: Andy! Why are you late?

Andy: There's a thingumybob in the High Street, sir.

Mr Mann: A what-did-you-say?

Andy: A thingumybob.

Mr Mann: A thingumy-what?

Andy: A watchamacallit, an oojamaflip!

Mr Mann: Stop! My head's going round and round! What is it doing?

Andy: It's breaking all the lampposts down, and using them for toothpicks.

Mr Mann: Andy –

Andy: It ate every hamburger in MacWimpeys, and then it ate MacWimpeys.

Mr Mann: Don't be silly –

Andy: It sat on the station and played trains with REAL TRAINS!

Mr Mann: You mustn't make up stories.

Andy: But sir, I'm not, I SAW it!

Andy: It sat on the town hall and squashed it flat.
Then the Mayor drove up in his big black
car and told it to stop, but it didn't.
It ate him.

Whole Class: *(Frightened)* Ooooh!

Andy: It swallowed him up like a jelly baby.
But it spat out his big gold chain.

Jason: What was it like?

Andy: It had great long horrible hairy arms,
and hands that could tear up a tank.

Jason: It's enough to give you the HEEBY-
JEEBIES!

Mr Mann: Andy, that will do!
I don't believe a word you've said,
let's hear no more about it.

Andy: But sir –

Mr Mann: Sit down at once!

(Mr Mann starts to call the register again.)

Mr Mann: Bernard?

Bernard: Here, sir.

Mr Mann: Claire?

Creepy Claire: Here, sir.

Mr Mann: Denise?

(There is no reply.)

Mr Mann: Denise? Where's Denise?

Whole Class: Don't know, sir.

Creepy Claire: Will she have to stand in the corner, sir?

(Denise rushes in late, very hot and bothered.)

Mr Mann: Denise! Why are you late?

Denise: A thingumybob's just stopped my bus.

Mr Mann: A what-did-you-say?

Denise: A thingumybob.

Mr Mann: A thingumy-what?

Denise: A watchamacallit, an oojamaflip!

Mr Mann: Stop! My head's going round and round!
What did it do?

Denise: It stopped the bus.
It sat in the road and made us stop.

Mr Mann: Denise –

Denise: It picked up the bus and waved it about
till we rattled like pennies in a piggy-
bank.

Mr Mann: Don't be silly –

Denise: Then it opened the door, and shook us all
out like sweets from a packet.

Mr Mann: You mustn't make up stories.

Denise: But sir, I'm not, I SAW it.
It bent the bus until it snapped in half,
and a policeman came up and told it to
stop, but it didn't.
It ate him.

Whole Class: *(Frightened)* Ooooooh!

Denise: It swallowed him up like a chocolate drop,
but it spat out his whistle and boots.

Jason: What was it like?

Denise: A huge hairy bottom all covered in fur
and a back like a big orange hill.

Andy: And great long horrible hairy arms,
and hands that could tear up a tank.

Jason: It's enough to give you the
COLLYWOBBLES!

Mr Mann: Denise, that will do!
I don't believe a word you've said,
let's hear no more about it.

Denise: But sir –

Mr Mann: Sit down at once!

(Mr Mann starts to call the register again.)

Mr Mann: Emma?

Emma: Here, sir.

Mr Mann: Frankie?

Frankie: Here, sir.

Mr Mann: Gabriel?

(There is no reply.)

Mr Mann: Gabriel? Where's Gabriel?

Whole Class: Don't know, sir.

Creepy Claire: Will he have to sit in the corridor, sir?

(Gabriel rushes in, very hot and bothered.)

Mr Mann: Gabriel! Why are you late?

Gabriel: There's a thingumybob in the park lake, sir.

Mr Mann: A what-did-you-say?

Gabriel: A thingumybob.

Mr Mann: A thingumy-what?

Gabriel: A watchamacallit, an oojamaflip!

Mr Mann: Stop! My head's going round and round! What is it doing?

Gabriel: The backstroke, I think.
It's splashing and sploshing and
swimming about.

Mr Mann: Gabriel –

Gabriel: It's frightened off the ducks and geese
and drunk the fountains dry.

Mr Mann: Don't be silly –

Gabriel: It's got a sky-blue bathing cap.

Mr Mann: You mustn't make up stories.

Gabriel: But sir, I'm not, I SAW it!

Mr Mann: And even if you saw this thing,
why should it make you late?

Gabriel: Because it was diving off the bridge
I cross to get to school,
and a park-keeper came up and told it to
stop, but it didn't.
It ate him.

Whole Class: (*Frightened*) Oooooooh!

Gabriel: It swallowed him up like an extra-strong mint, but it spat out his cap and his stick.

Jason: What was it like?

Gabriel: Enormous, wrinkly, scaly feet, all floppy and webbed like a duck's.

Denise: A huge hairy bottom all covered in fur and a back like a big orange hill.

Andy: And great long horrible hairy arms, and hands that could tear up a tank.

Jason: It's enough to give you the DITHERING DOO-DAHS!

Mr Mann: Gabriel, that will do!
I don't believe a word you've said,
let's hear no more about it.

Gabriel: But sir –

Mr Mann: Sit down at once!

(Mr Mann starts to call the register again.)

Mr Mann: Helen?

Helen: Here, sir.

Mr Mann: Katy?

Katy: Here, sir.

Mr Mann: Louise?

(There is no reply.)

Mr Mann: Louise? Where's Louise?

Whole Class: Don't know, sir.

Creepy Claire: Will she have to lose her break, sir?

(Louise rushes in late, very hot and bothered.)

Mr Mann: Louise! Why are you late?

Louise: A thingumybob's just eaten Dad's car.

Mr Mann: A what-did-you-say?

Louise: A thingumybob.

Mr Mann: A thingumy-what?

Louise: A watchamacallit, an oojamaflip!

Mr Mann: Stop! My head's going round and round!
What did it do?

Louise: Just as we went to get in the car,
it picked it up.

Mr Mann: Louise –

Louise: It pulled off the tyres and chewed them
up like Liquorice Allsorts.

Mr Mann: Don't be silly –

Louise: Then it bit off the bonnet and doors.

Mr Mann: You mustn't make up stories.

Louise: But sir, I'm not, I SAW it.
It gobbled it up like a stick of rock,
but it spat out the golf bag dad keeps in
the boot.

Whole Class: (*frightened*) Ooooooooooh!

Jason: What was it like?

Louise: A dirty big mouth, all slobber and fangs, and its breath could strip paint off the wall.

Gabriel: Enormous, wrinkly, scaly feet, all floppy and webbed like a duck's

Denise: A huge hairy bottom all covered in fur and a back like a big orange hill.

Andy: And great long horrible hairy arms, and hands that could tear up a tank.

Jason: It's enough to give you the SCREAMING HAB-DABS!

Mr Mann:	Louise, that will do!
	I don't believe a word you've said,
	let's hear no more about it.
Louise:	But sir –
Mr Mann:	Sit down at once!
	(Mr Mann starts to call the register again.)
Mr Mann:	Michaela?
Michaela:	Here, sir.
Mr Mann:	Peter?
Peter:	Here, sir.
Mr Mann:	Surinder?
	(There is no reply.)
Mr Mann:	Surinder? Where's Surinder?
Whole Class:	Don't know, sir.
Creepy Claire:	Will she have to see the Head, sir?
	(Surinder rushes in late, very hot and bothered.)

Mr Mann: Surinder! Why are you late?

Surinder: There's a thingumybob in the playground, sir.

Mr Mann: A what-did-you-say?

Surinder: A thingumybob.

Mr Mann: A thingumy-what?

Surinder: A watchamacallit, an oojamaflip!

Mr Mann: Stop! My head's going round and round! What is it doing?

Surinder: It's eating the coal
and pulling the wheels off the bikes
in the sheds.

Mr Mann: Surinder –

Surinder: I'm not too sure what else it's done,
but the nursery's very quiet today.

Mr Mann: I've heard about enough –

Surinder: Its big fat belly was blocking the gate –
I had to climb over the wall.

Mr Mann: You're driving me round the bend!

Surinder: But, sir, I SAW it!
The caretaker came and told it to shift,
but it didn't.
It ate him.

Whole Class: (frightened) Oooooooooooh!

Surinder: It swallowed him up like a strawberry.
But it spat out his bucket and mop.

Jason: What was it like?

Surinder: A massive red belly as soft as marshmallow.

Louise: A dirty big mouth, all slobber and fangs, and its breath could strip paint off the wall.

Gabriel: Enormous, wrinkly, scaly feet, all floppy and webbed like a duck's.

Denise: A huge hairy bottom all covered in fur and a back like a big orange hill.

Andy: And great long horrible hairy arms, and hands that could tear up a tank.

Jason: It's enough to give you –

(But before Jason can go on, Mr Mann interrupts.)

Mr Mann: I don't want to hear any more!

Andy, Denise, Gabriel, Louise and Surinder:	But sir –
Mr Mann:	I know, you SAW it! I don't want to hear any more about Thingumybobs, Watchamacallits, So and sos, What-have-yous, Thingymajigs, Tiddly-pushes *or* Oojamaflips. *Do I make myself perfectly clear?*
Whole Class:	(*Meekly*) Yes, Mr Mann. (*But then Jason looks out of the window …*)
Jason:	Sir, sir, ooooh sir –
Mr Mann:	Well?
Jason:	There's a thingumybob at the window, sir. (*The whole class crowds to the window to look.*)

Surinder: It is, look. Great big eyes like paddling pools, and a massive red belly as soft as marshmallow.

Louise: A dirty big mouth, all slobber and fangs, and its breath could strip paint off the wall.

Gabriel: Enormous, wrinkly, scaly feet, all floppy and webbed like a duck's.

Denise: A huge hairy bottom all covered in fur and a back like a big orange hill.

Andy: And great long horrible hairy arms, and hands that could tear up a tank.

Mr Mann: I've had about enough of this. Whatever it is, I'm going to go and sort it out.

(Mr Mann slaps his hand on his desk, picks up his coat and umbrella, and storms out of the classroom. The children look at each other, amazed. There is a moment's silence, then from behind the closed door come more horrible and revolting sounds than anyone could possibly imagine.)

Jason: (*Whispers*) Did you see that?

Creepy Claire: The Thingumybob's gone and eaten sir.

Surinder: It looked at him with its great big eyes –

Andy: It picked him up in its great long hands –

Louise: It popped him into its dirty big mouth –

Gabriel: But it spat out his umbrella and specs.

(Miss Pelling comes in.)

Miss Pelling: What's going on? Get back to your desks. Where's Mr Mann?

(All the pupils shuffle their feet and look at the floor.)

Miss Pelling: Well? What's the matter?

Denise: The Thingumybob has eaten him.

Miss Pelling: The what-did-you say?

Andy: The Thingumybob.

Miss Pelling: The Thingumy-what?

Louise: The Watchamacallit –

Gabriel: The Oojamaflip –

Miss Pelling: Stop! My head's going round and round! What is it?

Whole Class: We don't know!

Creepy Claire: But we can tell you what it looks like.

Jason: It's got –

Surinder: Great big eyes like paddling pools and a massive red belly as soft as marshmallow.

Louise: A dirty big mouth, all slobber and fangs, and its breath could strip paint off the wall.

Gabriel: Enormous, wrinkly, scaly feet, all floppy and webbed like a duck's.

Denise: A huge hairy bottom all covered in fur and a back like a big orange hill.

Andy: And great long horrible hairy arms, and hands that could tear up a tank.

Creepy Claire:	And it EATS people!
Miss Pelling:	What sort of people?
Andy:	It eats mayors –
Denise:	And policemen –
Gabriel:	And park-keepers –
Surinder:	And caretakers –
Creepy Claire:	And TEACHERS!
Miss Pelling:	Oh. Ah. And where is it now?
Louise:	*(Pointing to the window)* Out there.
	(Miss Pelling very slowly turns and looks out of the window, and all the pupils do the same.)
Thingumybob:	*(From outside)* Ha, ha, ha, ha, ha!
	(Miss Pelling and the pupils all "freeze" perfectly still.)
	THE END. (We hope!)

Choosing Parts

The parts of Mr Mann, Andy, Denise, Gabriel, Louise and Surinder should be played by confident readers.

The parts of Miss Pelling, Creepy Claire and Jason are not quite so demanding. The other named characters have only to react as their names are called and as the Thingumybob's deeds are described.

Putting On the Play

You may wish to put on a performance of the play, rather than just reading it. The following suggestions may provide you with a starting point for your own ideas about staging a production. Obviously, the use you make of these suggestions will vary depending on the time and resources available to your school.

For permission to put on a profit-making performance of *Thingumybob*, please contact the Editorial Department, Ginn & Co. Ltd, Prebendal House, Parson's Fee, Aylesbury, Bucks HP20 2QY.

(There is no need to apply for permission if you are not charging an entrance fee, but please let us know if you are putting on any performance of this play, as we would be interested to hear about it.)

Staging

The play could be put on in any sufficiently large space. It would be interesting if the audience sat at desks in among the characters, so that they too could react and become part of the action.

Costumes

These should be kept very simple. **Mr Mann** will wear trousers and a jacket. He will need to have a coat to hand for when he leaves the classroom. **Creepy Claire** should be more neatly turned out than any normal person could be. In schools with a uniform, Claire will have everything. And it will all have been ironed. **Miss Pelling** can wear a skirt and blouse.

Everyone else can simply wear their normal school clothes. **Andy**, **Denise**, **Gabriel**, **Louise** and **Surinder** should come in wearing coats and carrying bags.

Props

Mr Mann will need a register, a ballpoint pen, an umbrella and a pair of glasses.

Sound Effects

There are two sound effects – the horrible thing happening to Mr Mann and the Thingumybob's laugh. Both could be done live, but they would probably be funnier if recorded on cassette so that they can be amplified. Recording the effects, particularly the first, should be a lot of fun!

Follow-up Work

Group Discussion

• Why do people make excuses? Do excuses help people to avoid trouble, or can they make the trouble worse?
  How do we know when people are making excuses?
  Do teachers sometimes think pupils are making excuses when they are really telling the truth?

- 'The Boy Who Cried Wolf' is a famous story about a boy who plays a joke on people once too often. How is this story similar to the story in Thingumybob, and how is it different?

Artwork

Ask the children to paint pictures or make a model of what they think the Thingumybob might look like.

Drama

Thought-Tracking

Reread the end of the play. Right at the end, Miss Pelling asks where the Thingumybob is now, and Louise points to the window and says, "Out there." Then everyone in the play has to freeze perfectly still.

While the class is standing still, the teacher should go round and tap each pupil on the shoulder in turn. Explain beforehand that when this happens, the children must say exactly what they are thinking (in character) at that moment. For instance, some might be thinking, "Poor Mr Mann, I do feel sorry for him!" or "How am I going to get home for lunch now?"

When everyone has said their thoughts aloud, talk about what was said.

Quick Thinking

Ask each member of the class in turn why they are late for school. Each must invent the most amazing reason he or she can think of. For example, "Well, I realised my hamster had escaped and I found it in the kitchen, but just then Mum called me, so I put it in the washing machine because its cage door was broken, and when I got back my sister had turned the washing machine on, so I had to rescue my hamster and give it the kiss of life..."

Monster Movement

If the Thingumybob is big enough to play trains with real trains, how does it move? Ask the children to think about the movements of large animals such as elephants and hippos. Then they should all try to move like the Thingumybob. Begin with walking, then progress to sitting down and getting up, and climbing over obstacles such as chairs and blocks.

What sorts of sounds go with the Thingumybob's movements? In small groups pupils can try to create the sounds the creature might make.

Ask the children to act out other scenes in the manner of a Thingumybob. For example, how would a Thingumybob go shopping? What would a Thingumybob policeman be like?

31